THE STORY BOX®

TAKE-ME-HOMES™

STORIES
AND ACTIVITIES
BLACKLINE
MASTERS

EARLY EMERGENT

The Story Box® Take-Me-Homes™ Stories and Activities
Blackline Masters: Early Emergent

©1999 Wright Group Publishing, Inc.

Line illustrations by Andrew Hess and Cary Pillo

The Wright Group
19201 120th Avenue NE
Bothell, WA 98011

Printed in the United States of America

10 9 8 7 6 5 4 3 2 1

ISBN: 0-322-00513-2

Contents

Take-Me-Homes™ for the Read-Togethers

Read-Togethers 1

Read-Togethers 2

Take-Me-Homes™ for Guided Reading Books

Set A

Set B

Set C

Set D

Introduction

The Story Box® Take-Me-Homes™ were created to enrich the school-to-home connection. These reproducible activities and stories enhance the family's connection to a child's learning. The take-home activities, each related to a shared reading book, encourage the child to retell and talk about the story with parents, siblings, and friends. The reproducible stories from guided reading provide a chance for the child to read alone or to read aloud to family members. The Take-Me-Homes not only strengthen school-to-home ties but also help give the child a feeling of ownership of books and reading.

For shared reading, the take-home activities are varied. Each is a hands-on project inspired by the book the child's class has been studying for the past five days. Students complete the activity at school and then take it home to share.

For guided reading, the take-home item is a reproduction of a book the child has read and discussed in a smaller group. This take-home version allows for more independent reading, which research shows is an essential element of reading success.

The letter on pages 4–5 will inform families about their children's reading at school, and encourage them to talk about and read stories with their children at home.

How to Use the Take-Me-Homes for the Read-Togethers

Copy the activities ahead of time. Some of the shared reading activities, such as the story wheels, require simple assembly. Follow the instructions on the activity page itself. Many of the activity pages can be copied multiple times for each student, to make a multi-page booklet. Following the shared reading lesson, give each student the take-home activity for that story. Have them complete the activity. Then encourage them to practice reading their work, and to take home their activities to share with family members.

How to Use the Take-Me-Homes for Guided Reading Books

Copy the blackline master and assemble the books ahead of time, if possible. The simple assembly instructions are on the next page. You may instead model how to assemble the books and have the children put them together. At the end of the guided reading lesson, make sure each child has a reproducible version of the book. Encourage the children to illustrate the cover and then color the pictures in the book. When their books are complete they can read them to a partner. Then they can take their books home to read to family members.

Assembly Instructions

for Guided Reading Books

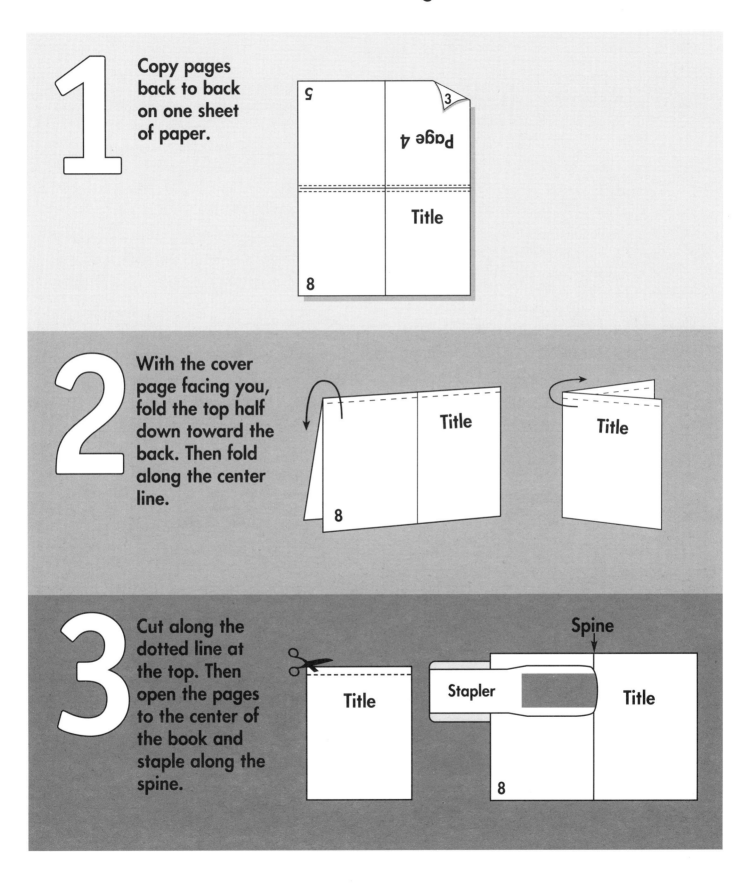

1 Copy pages back to back on one sheet of paper.

2 With the cover page facing you, fold the top half down toward the back. Then fold along the center line.

3 Cut along the dotted line at the top. Then open the pages to the center of the book and staple along the spine.

Dear Families,

This year your child will be using The Story Box® Take-Me-Homes™. These are activities and stories we will make at school that your child will take home to keep and read to you. Some of the Take-Me-Homes are activities that will help your child retell Story Box books we have read together at school. Some of them are small versions of Story Box books that your child has read at school.

Reading with your child, and having your child read to you, is the best way to ensure his or her success as a reader. Please set aside time to enjoy the Take-Me-Homes together. Help your child make a special place to keep the Take-Me-Homes. You can decorate a cereal box, a soap box, or a small plastic crate to hold them.

Have fun reading with your child!

Sincerely,

Estimadas familias:

Este año su niño/a utilizará las hojas de Take-Me-Homes™ (Llévame a casa) de Story Box®. Éste es un conjunto de hojas de actividades y cuentos que se harán en la escuela y que su niño/a llevará a casa para guardar y leérselos a usted. Algunas de las hojas de Take-Me-Homes (Llévame a casa) son actividades que le ayudarán a su niño/a a contar de nuevo los cuentos de Story Box que habremos leído en la escuela. Algunos de los cuentos son cortas versiones de los libros de Story Box que su niño/a habrá leído en la escuela.

La mejor forma de asegurar el éxito de su niño/a como lector/a es por medio de leer con él/ella o al escucharle a su niño/a que le lea a usted. Por favor dedique una cierta cantidad de tiempo para disfrutar las hojas de Take-Me-Homes (Llévame a casa) con su niño/a. Ayúdele a su niño/a a identificar un lugar especial donde él/ella pueda guardar las hojas de Take-Me-Homes (Llévame a casa). Tal vez puedan decorar una caja de cereal, una caja de detergente o una caja pequeña de plástico para guardarlas.

¡Disfrute la lectura con su niño/a!

Atentamente,

TAKE-ME-HOMES™

FOR THE
READ-TOGETHERS

The Farm Concert

by _____

" _____ , _____ ,"

went the _____ .

In a Dark, Dark Wood

by _____

Teacher Instructions: Copy this page and the next onto separate sheets for each child. Have the children cut the pictures apart, color them, and place them in sequence to retell the story.

Permission is given to teachers who purchase Story Box® pupil editions to reproduce these pages for classroom and take-home use only. ©1999 Wright Group Publishing, Inc.

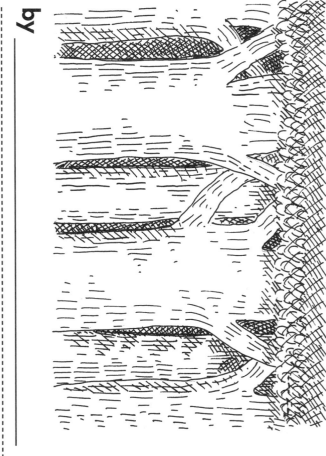

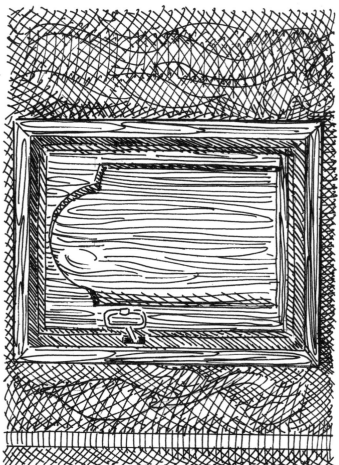

The Jigaree

 _____

Teacher Instructions: Have each child write his or her name in the blank and illustrate this page to make a cover. Then have the children fill in the blank on the next page and illustrate their jigarees. Help students staple the pages together along the left side. Copy the next page multiple times to make a longer booklet. Invite the children to read their booklets.

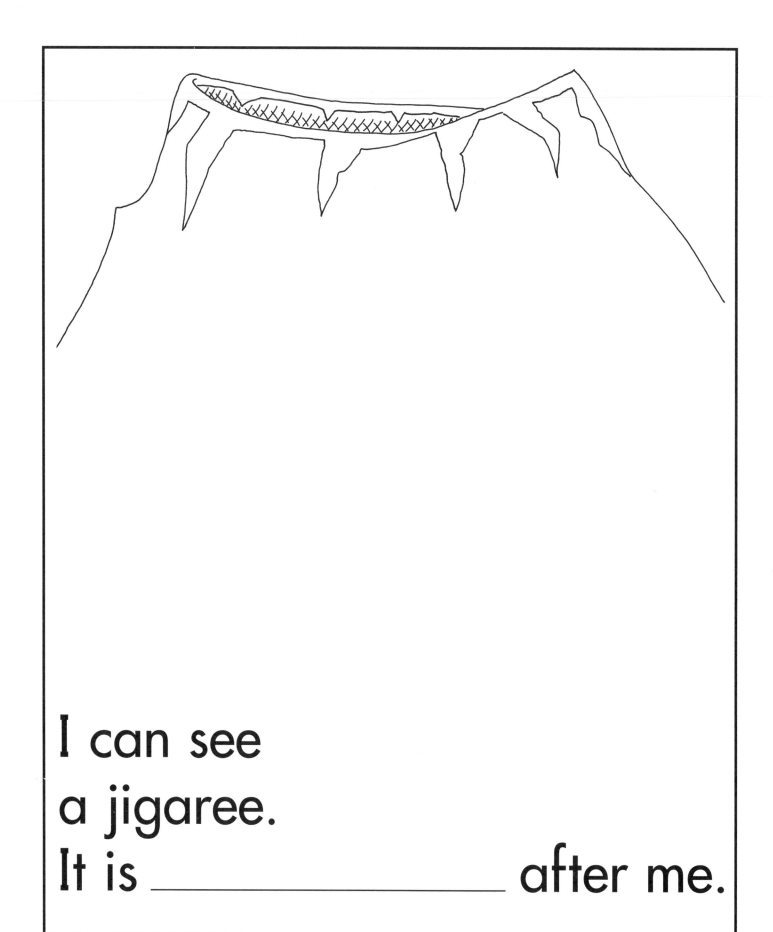

I can see
a jigaree.
It is _____ after me.

The Monsters' Party

by _____

What can
this little monster do?

✂ -

It can _____ .
That's what it can do.

Teacher Instructions: Copy this page and the next onto two separate sheets for each child. Have the children cut along the dotted lines, fill in the blanks, illustrate the pages, and staple the pages together along the left side. Copy the next page multiple times to make a longer booklet. Invite the children to read their booklets.

It can _____.

That's what it can do.

- -

It can _____.

That's what it can do.

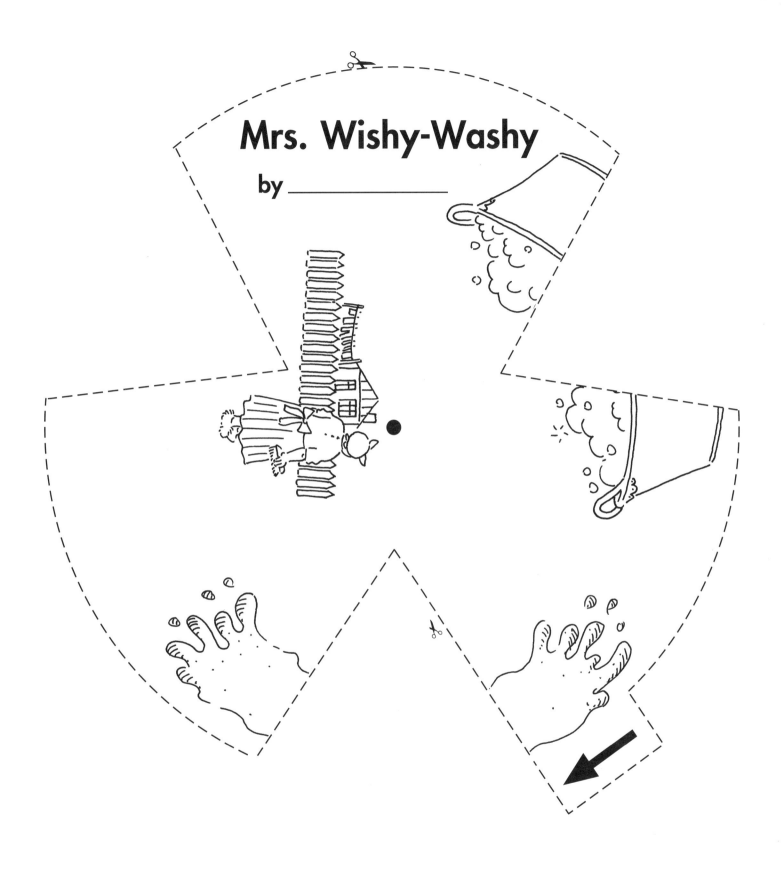

Mrs. Wishy-Washy

by _____

Teacher Instructions: Copy this page and the next onto two separate sheets for each child. Have each child write his or her name in the blank, color the pictures, and cut along the dotted lines. Help the children assemble the wheels by inserting a brad in the center. Invite the children to turn their wheels and retell the story.

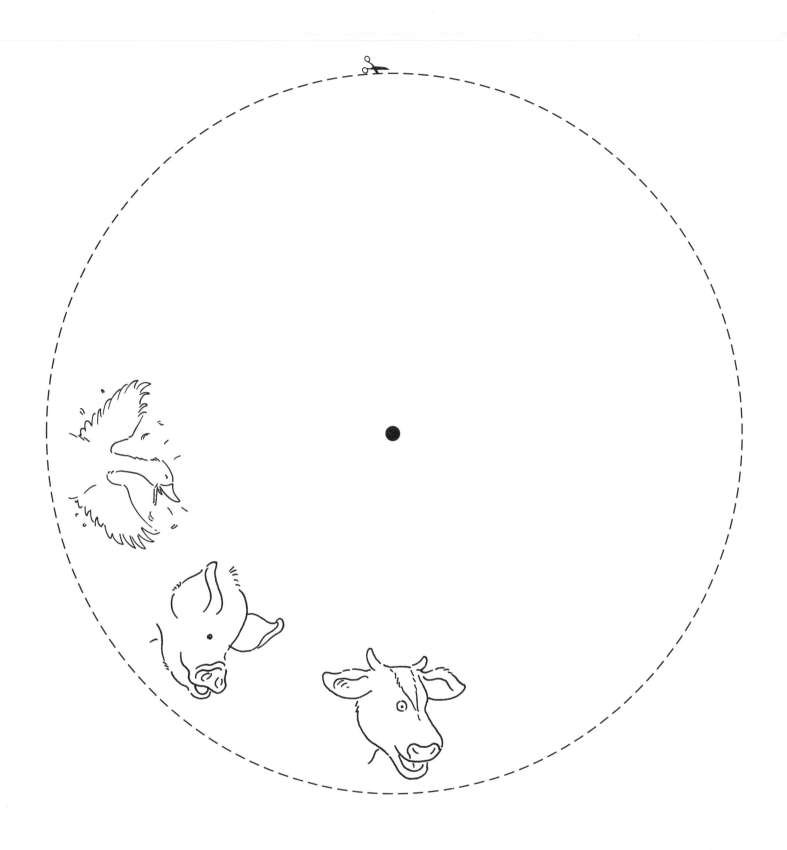

Sing a Song

by _____

✂ -

Teacher Instructions: Copy this page and the next onto two separate sheets for each child. Have each child write his or her name in the blank. Then have them cut apart and color the pictures, and place them in sequence to retell the story.

✂ -

To Town

by _____

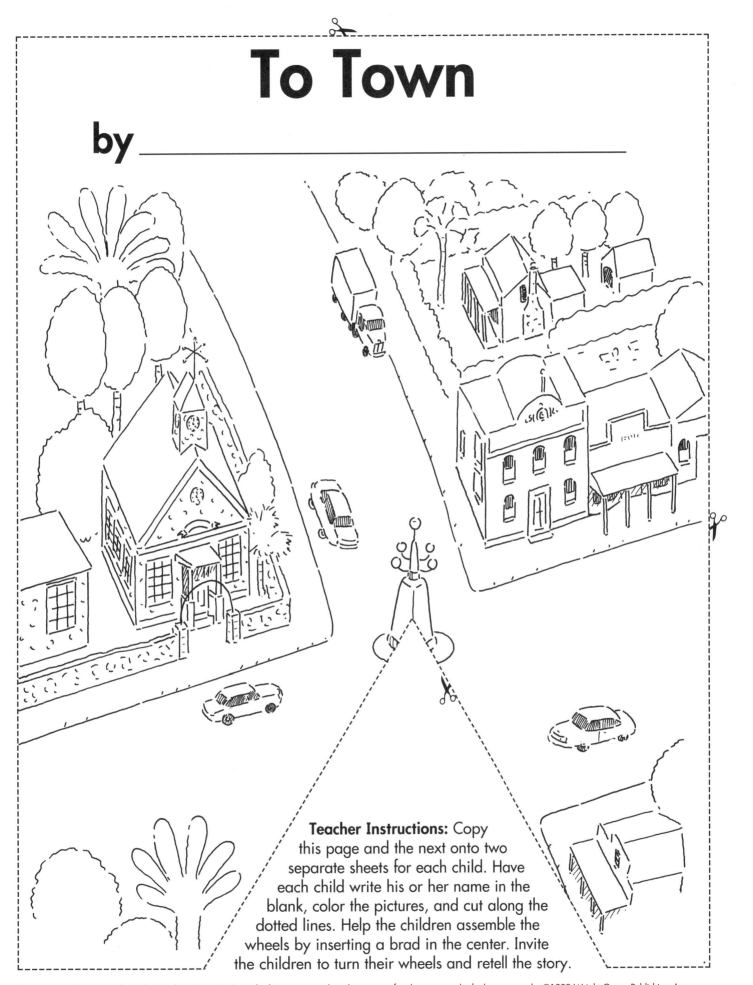

Teacher Instructions: Copy this page and the next onto two separate sheets for each child. Have each child write his or her name in the blank, color the pictures, and cut along the dotted lines. Help the children assemble the wheels by inserting a brad in the center. Invite the children to turn their wheels and retell the story.

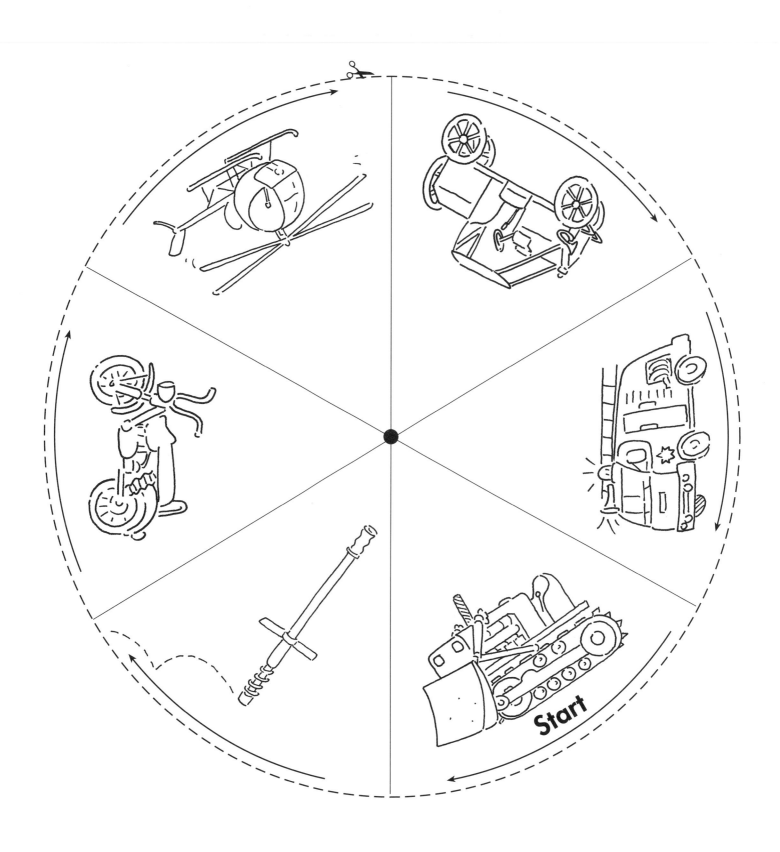

Start

Yes, Ma'am

by _____

✂ -

Did you feed my _____?

Teacher Instructions: Copy this page and the next onto two separate sheets for each child. Have the children cut along the dotted lines, fill in the blanks, illustrate the pages, and staple the pages together along the left side. Copy the next page multiple times to make a longer booklet. Invite children to read their booklets.

Did you feed my _____?

✂️--

Did you feed my _____?

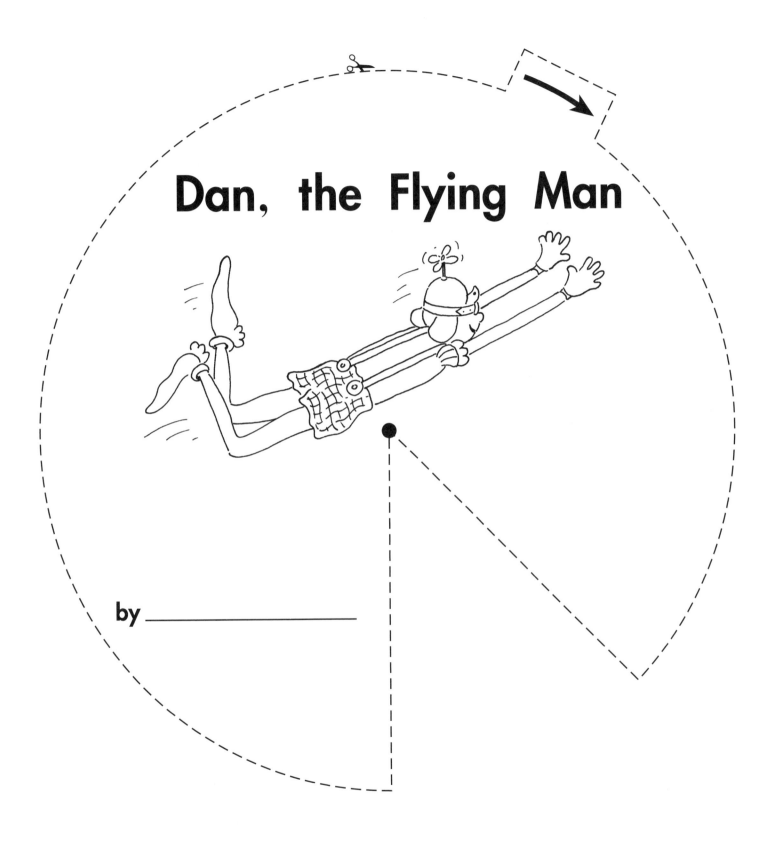

Dan, the Flying Man

by _____

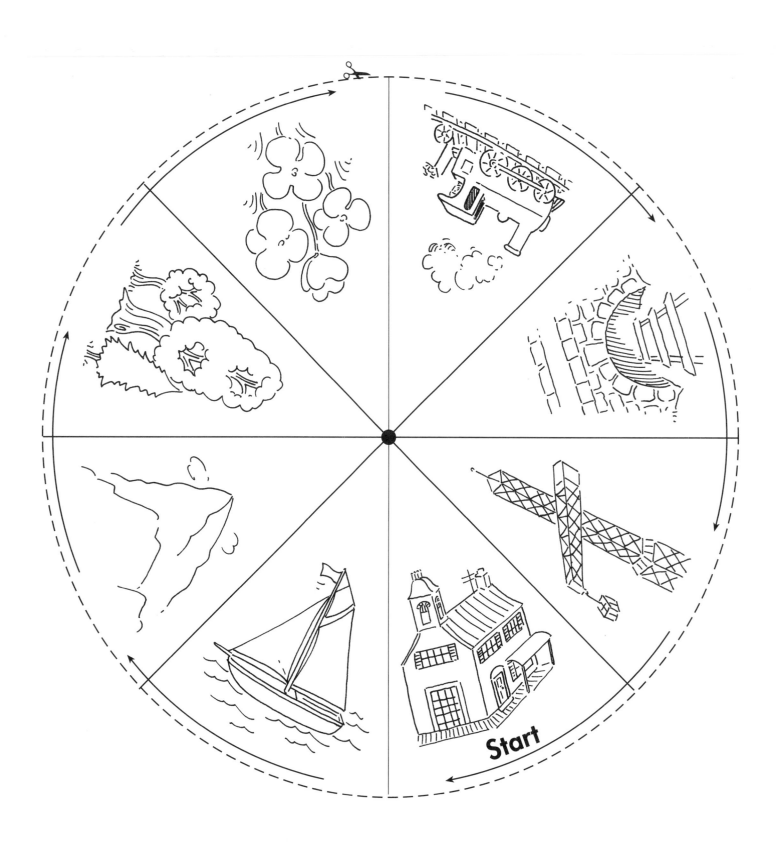

Start

Grandpa, Grandpa

by _____

What will we fish for?

1 one _____

What will we fish for?

2 two _____

What will we fish for?

3 three _____

Hairy Bear

by

Teacher Instructions: Have each child write his or her name in the blank and illustrate this page. Then have them cut apart and color the pictures on the next page, and place them in sequence to retell the story.

Meanies

by _____

Teacher Instructions: Copy this page and the next onto two separate sheets for each child. Have each child write his or her name in the blank, color the pictures, and cut along the dotted lines. Help the children assemble the wheels by inserting a brad in the center. Invite the children to turn their wheels and retell the story.

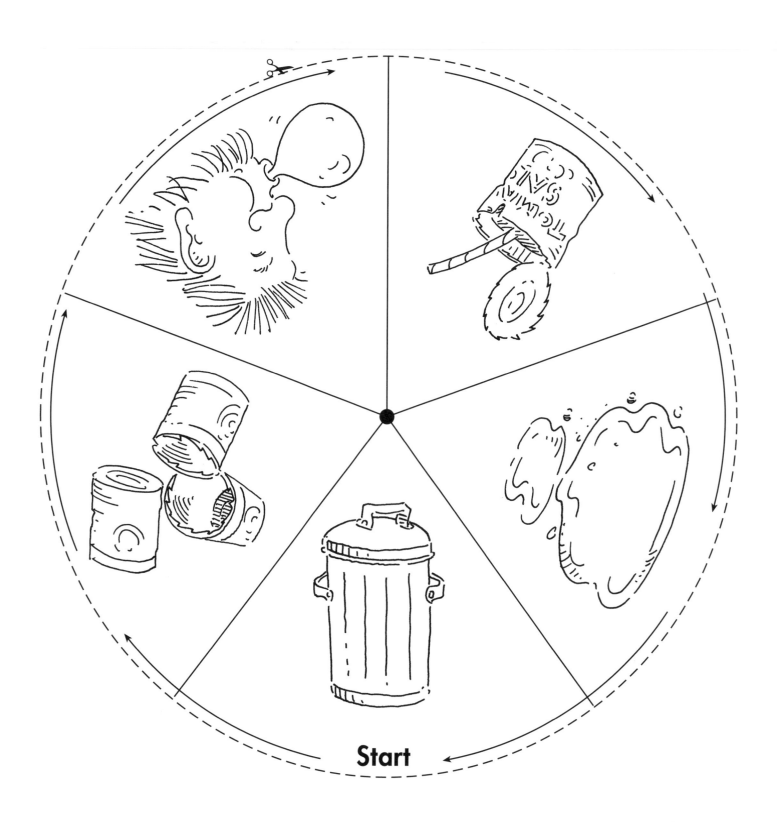

Start

Poor Old Polly

by

Teacher Instructions: Have each child write his or her name in the blank and illustrate this page to make a cover. Then have the children fill in the blanks on the next page and illustrate the page. Help students staple the pages together along the left side. Copy the next page multiple times to make a longer booklet. Invite the children to read their booklets.

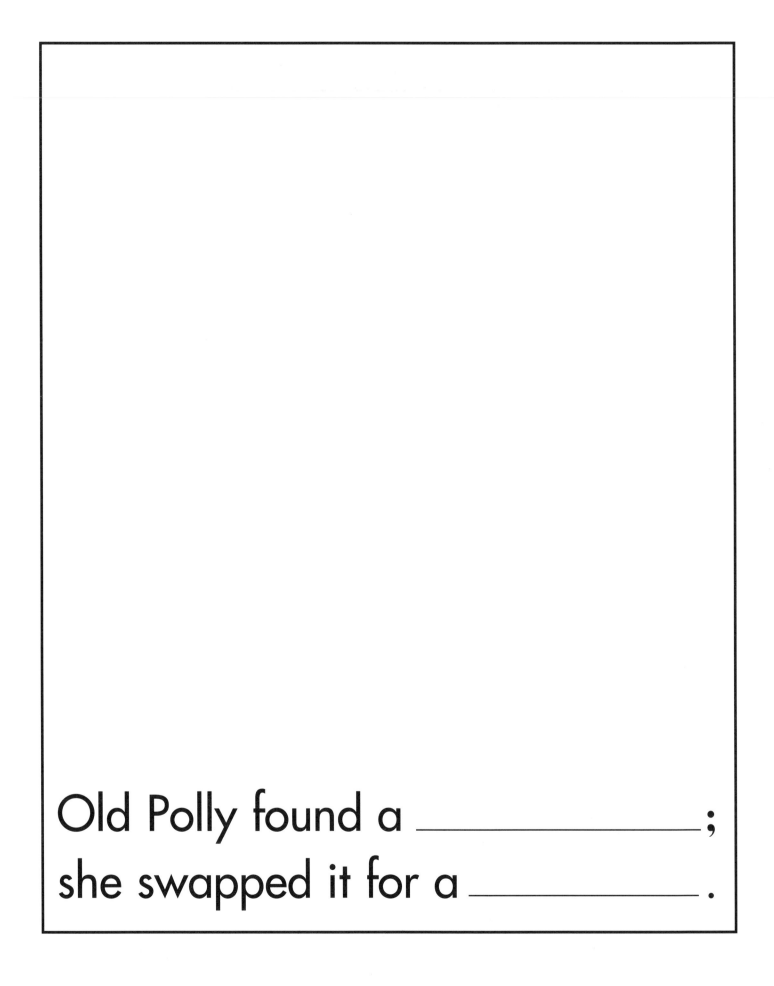

Old Polly found a _____ ;
she swapped it for a _____ .

The Red Rose

by _____

- -

"Ah," said a _____ ,
"I see a _____ ."

Teacher Instructions: Copy this page and the next onto two separate sheets for each child. Have the children cut along the dotted lines, fill in the blanks, illustrate the pages, and staple the pages together along the left side. Copy the next page multiple times to make a longer booklet. Invite the children to read their booklets.

"Ah," said a _____ ,
"I see a _____ ."

✂ -

"Ah," said a _____ ,
"I see a _____ ."

Three Little Ducks

by _____

Teacher Instructions: Have each child write his or her name in the blank and illustrate this page to make a cover. Then have the children illustrate the story's events inside the "eggs" on the next page and retell the story by following the picture map.

Three Little Ducks

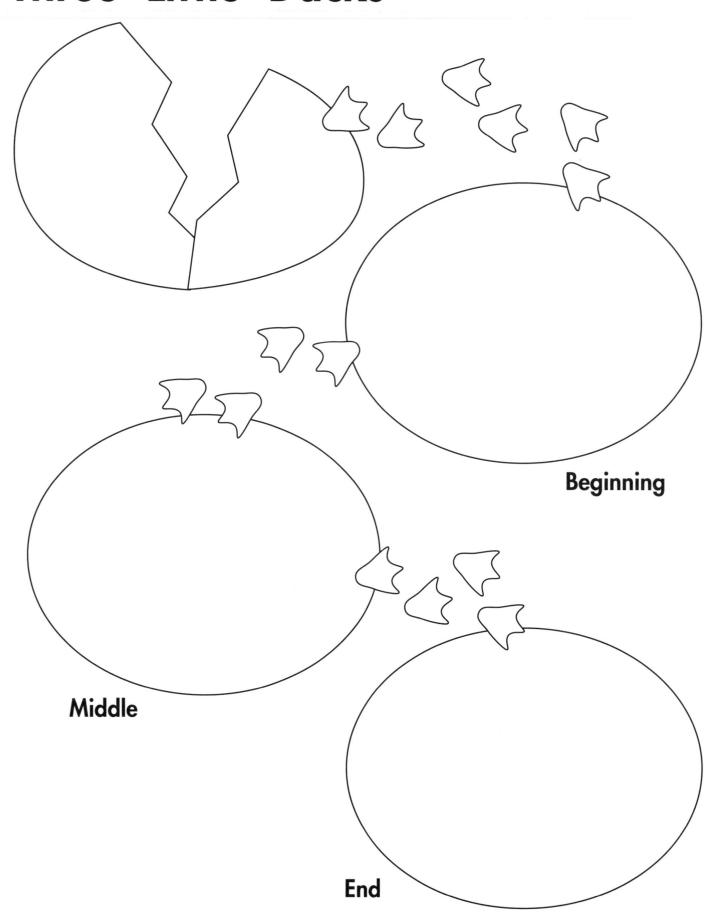

Beginning

Middle

End

Who Will Be My Mother?

by _____

Teacher Instructions: Have each child write his or her name in the blank and illustrate this page to make a cover. Then have the children color the pictures on the next page and retell the story by following the picture map.

Who Will Be My Mother?

TAKE-ME-HOMES™

FOR GUIDED READING BOOKS

"Happy Birthday, Brenda!"

Story by Joy Cowley

a book,

Brenda's Birthday

Fold here

✂ Cut after folding ✂

a flower,

3

a pencil,

a kitten,

6

Copy with this side up

Cut after folding

Cut after folding

Brenda got a card,

2

and a kiss.

7

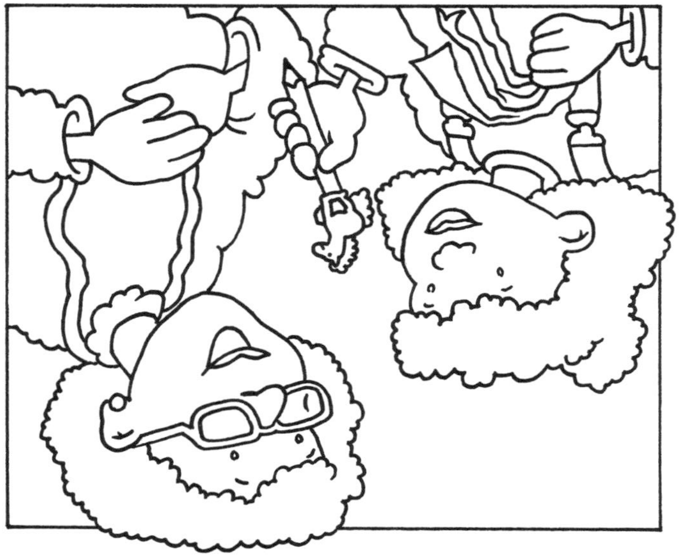

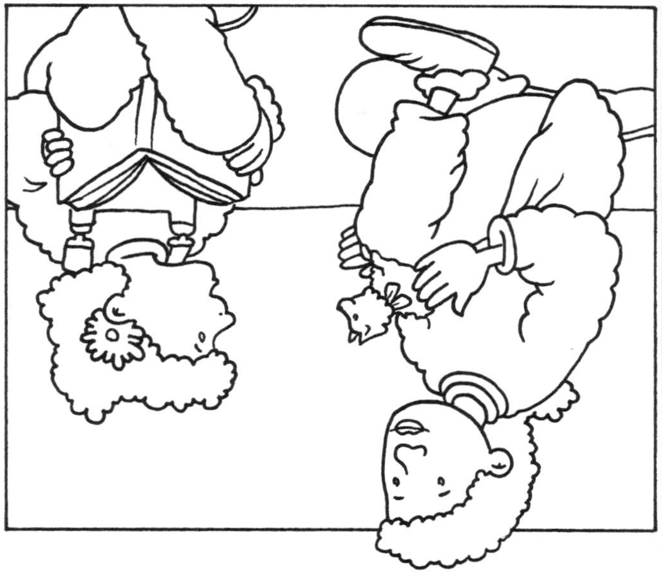

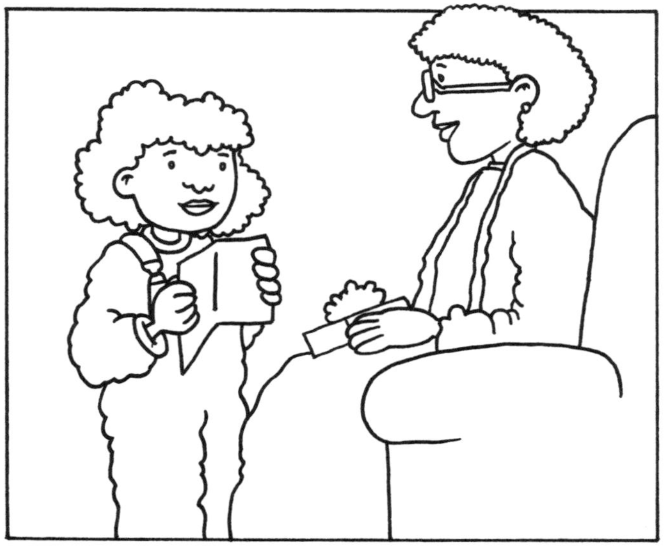

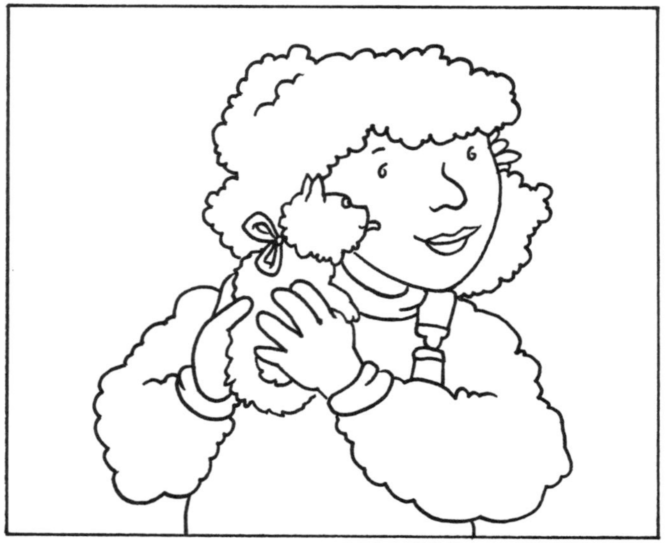

✂ Cut after folding

✂ Cut after folding

4
"Mmm-mmm!"
said Mom.

5
"Mmm!"
said Dad.

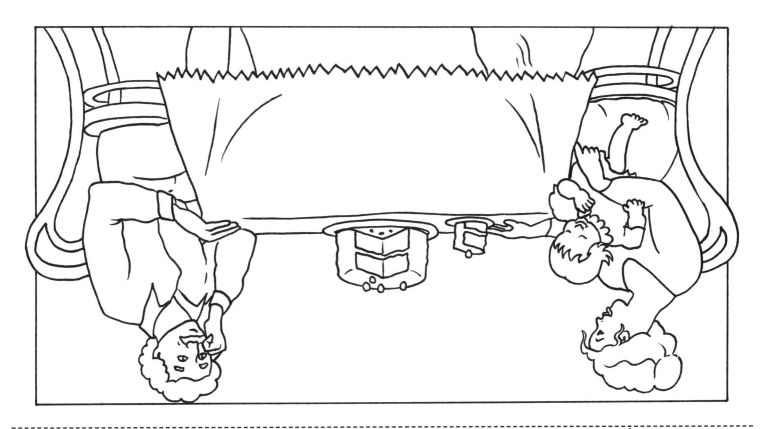

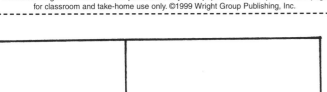

"More! More! More!"
they said.

8

45

The Chocolate Cake

Story by June Melser

"M-m-m-m-m!"
said Grandpa.

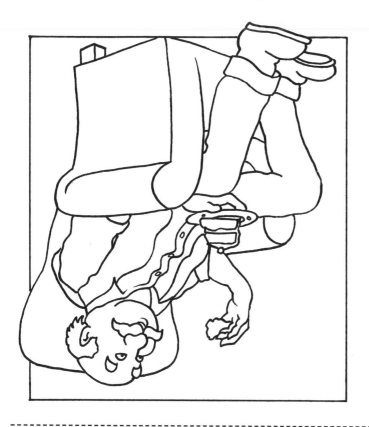

"M-m-m-m-m-m-m-m-m!"
said Baby.

▲ **Copy with this side up**

✂ **Cut after folding**

✂ **Cut after folding**

"M-m-m-m-m-m-m-m!"
said Grandma.

2   46

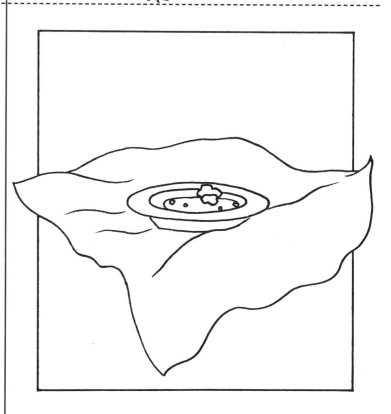

It's all gone!

7

Tickle his toes.

Tickle his legs.

▲ Copy with this side up

✂ Cut after folding

✂ Cut after folding

and that will be
the end of him.

If You Meet
a Dragon...

 Story by Joy Cowley

Tickle his nose.

Tickle his tail.

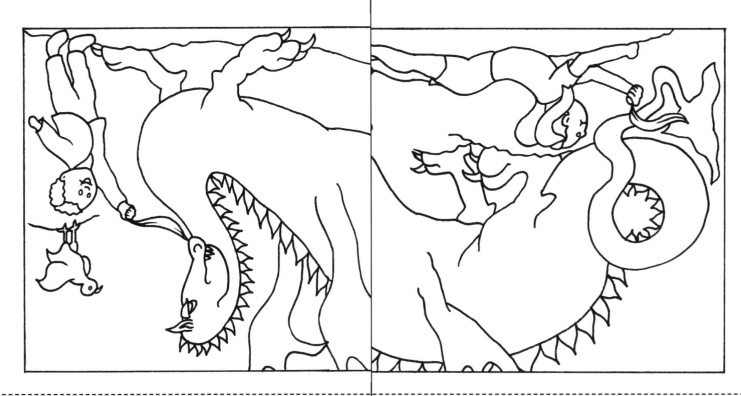

▲ Copy with this side up

Cut after folding ✂

✂ Cut after folding

Tickle his back.

Tickle his chin...

and a stick

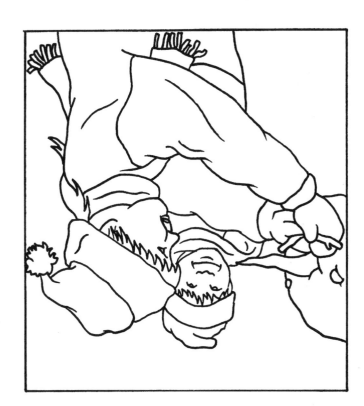

and a mouth

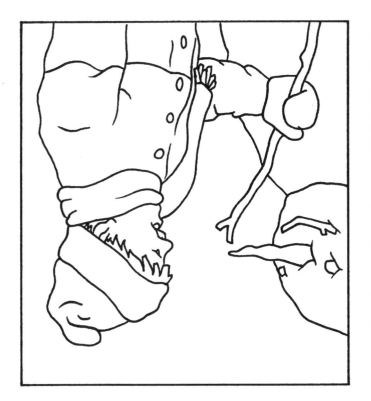

Copy with this side up

Cut after folding

✂ Cut after folding

A snowman!

Snowman

Story by Joy Cowley

and a nose

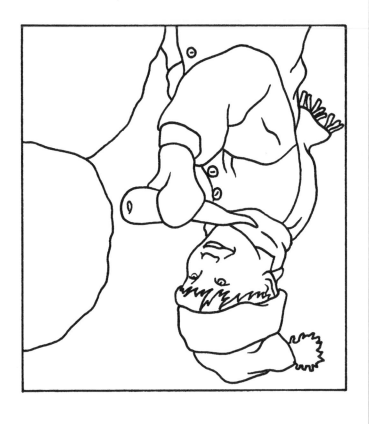

and a scarf

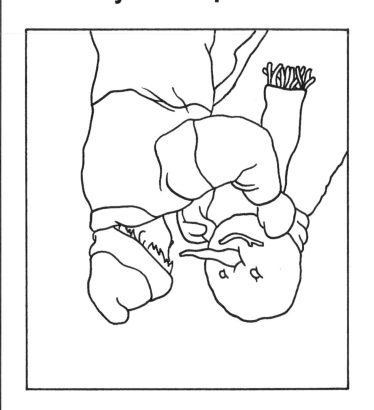

Cut after folding ✂

✂ Cut after folding

Two eyes

and a hat.

I cry.

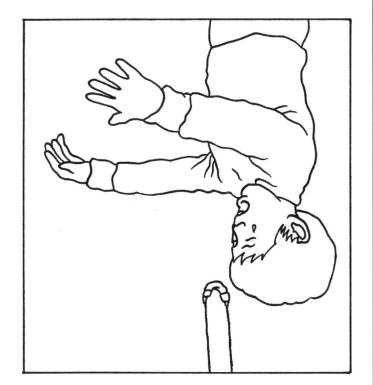

I fall.

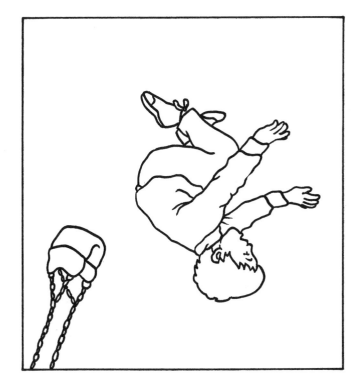

✂ Cut after folding

✂ **Cut after folding**

Swing

I swing.

Story by Joy Cowley

I swing. I swing.

I get a hug.

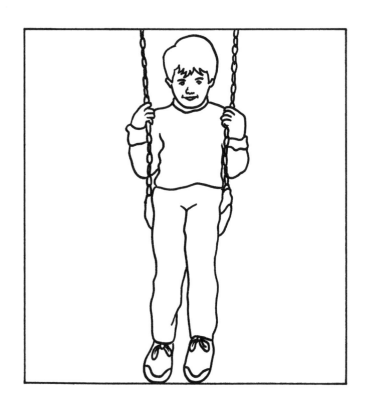

I swing. I swing.

I swing.

I smile.

A taxi went by.

A police car went by.

▲ **Copy with this side up**

✂ **Cut after folding**

✂ **Cut after folding**

"Dad! Dad!"

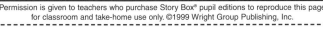

Waiting

Story by Joy Cowley

A truck went by.

A fire engine went by.

▲ Copy with this side up

✂ Cut after folding

✂ Cut after folding

A bus went by.

A red car stopped.

We roll.

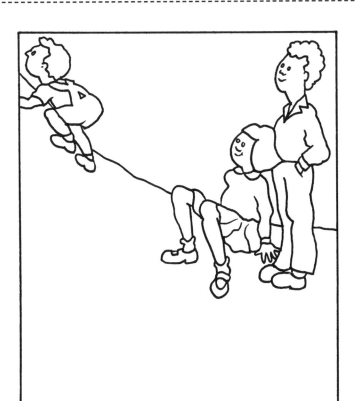

We fall.

✂ Cut after folding

✂ Cut after folding

Then we climb up again.

The Big Hill

Story by Joy Cowley

8

55

We run down.

We crash.

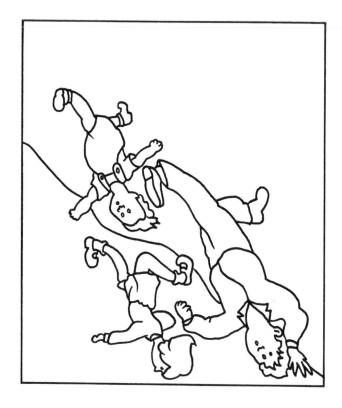

We climb up.

We laugh.

Four meanies
on the bridge.

Five meanies
on the bridge.

Cut after folding

✂ Cut after folding

The Bridge

Story by Joy Cowley

**Six meanies
in the water.**

Three meanies
on the bridge.

Six meanies
on the bridge.

▲ **Copy with this side up**

✂ **Cut after folding**

✂ **Cut after folding**

**Two meanies
on the bridge.**

Oh-oh!

Gotcha!

This is the blue box.

✂ Cut after folding
Fold after folding

Story by Joy Cowley

The "Gotcha" Box

This is the yellow box.

This is the orange box.

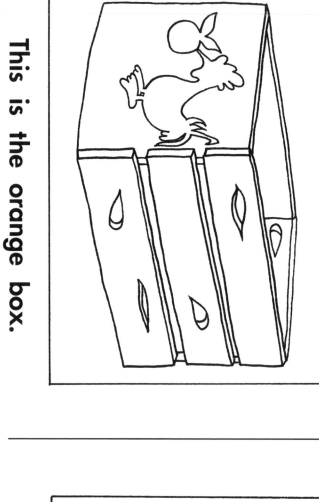

This is the "gotcha" box.

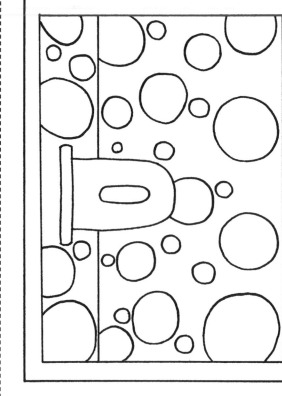

✂ Cut after folding

✂ Cut after folding

This is the red box.

This is the green box.

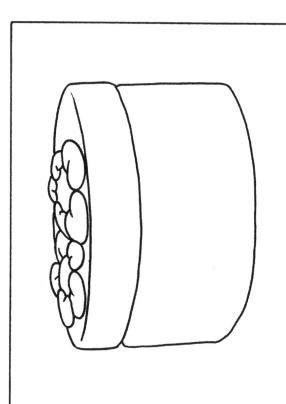

Put some meat
on it.

Put some pickles
on it.

✂ Cut after folding

▲ Copy with this side up

✂ Cut after folding

Now take a bite.
Yum, yum!

A Monster Sandwich

Story by Joy Cowley

Put some cheese
on it.

Put some tomatoes
on it.

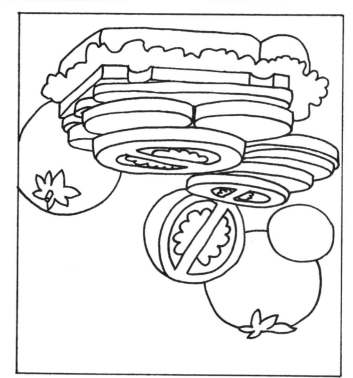

▲ Copy with this side up

✂ Cut after folding

✂ Cut after folding

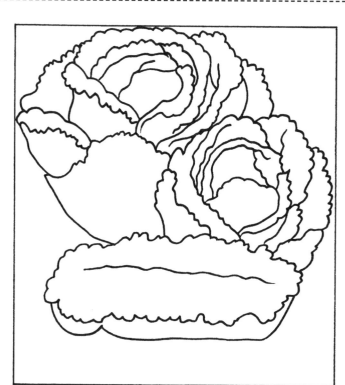

Put some lettuce on it.

Put some bread on it.

The duck is in the tub.

The dog is in the tub.

▲ Copy with this side up

Cut after folding ✂

✂ Cut after folding

Mrs. Wishy-Washy's Tub

Wishy-washy!
Wishy-washy!

 Story by Joy Cowley

8

The pig is in the tub.

The water is in the tub.

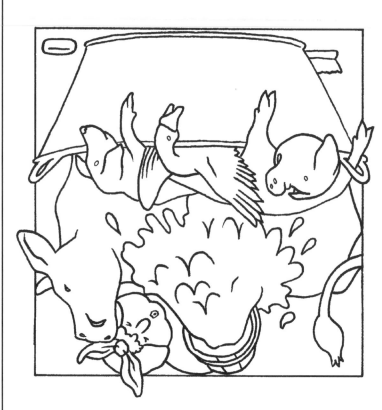

▲ Copy with this side up

✂ Cut after folding

✂ Cut after folding

The cow is in the tub.

The soap is in the tub.

Duck went ha-ha-ha.

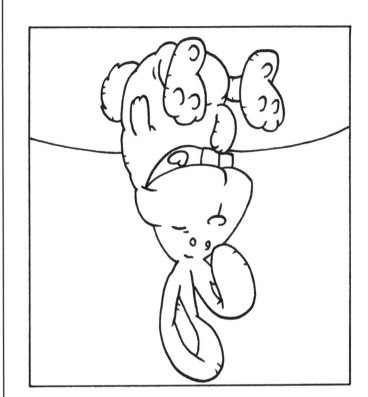

Rabbit went ha-ha-ha.

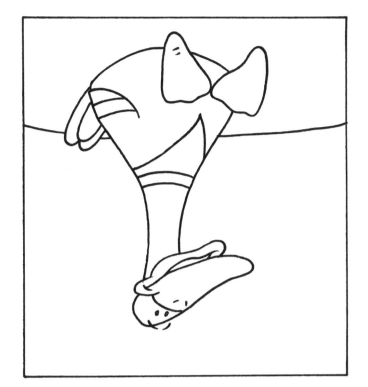

▲ **Copy with this side up**

✂ Cut after folding

✂ **Cut after folding**

Rat's Funny Story

Story by Joy Cowley

"Not funny!" said Rat.

Hen went ha-ha-ha.

Pig went ha-ha-ha,
ha-ha-ha

▲ **Copy with this side up**

✂ **Cut after folding**

✂ **Cut after folding**

Rat told a funny story.

and fell on Rat.

Now I can fly.
Zoom! Zoom!

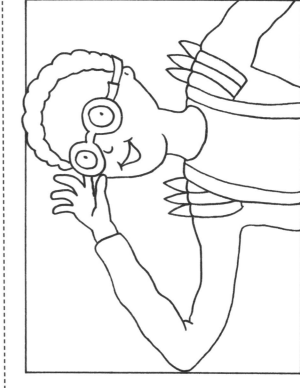

I put on my flying goggles.

Story by Joy Cowley

Dan Gets Dressed

Cut after folding ✂

Cut after folding ✂

I put on my flying shoes.

I put on my flying gloves.

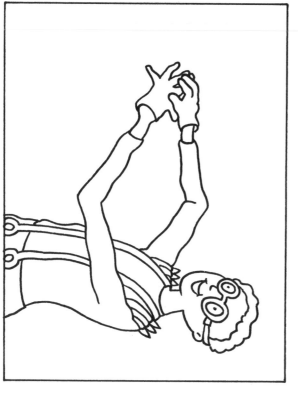

I put on my zoom-zoom hat.

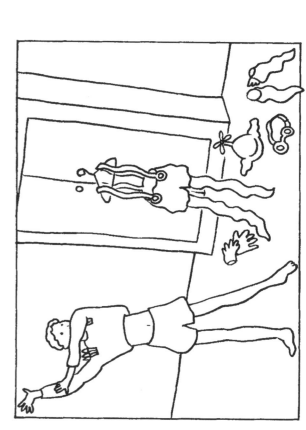

I put on my flying pants.

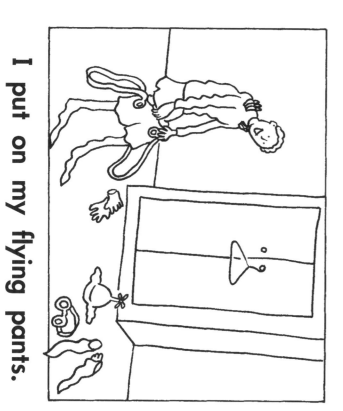

I put on my flying shirt.

Cat is frightened
of the dog.

Bird is frightened
of the cat.

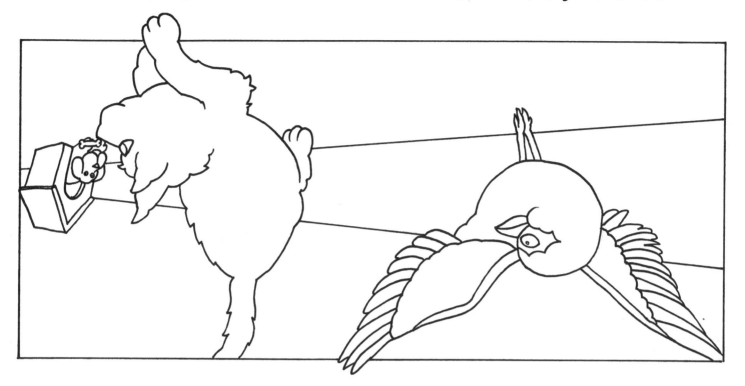

✂ Cut after folding

✂ **Cut after folding**

Frightened

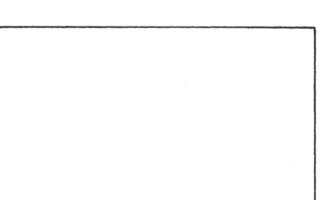

What are you frightened of?

 Story by Joy Cowley

Spider is frightened
of the bird.

Dog is frightened
of Mr. Grump.

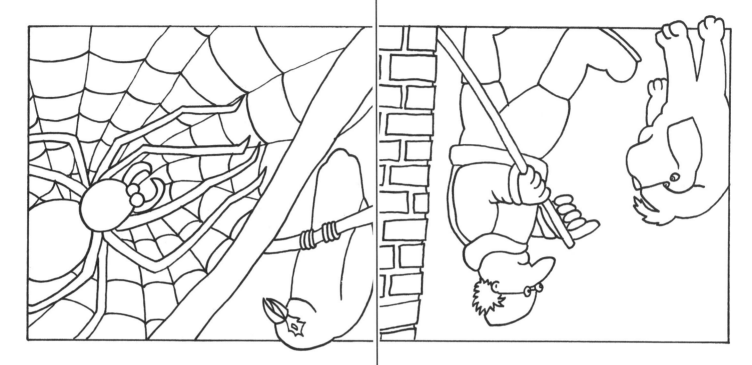

▲ **Copy with this side up**

Cut after folding

✂ **Cut after folding**

Fly is frightened
of the spider.

Mr. Grump is
frightened of the dark.

Jump over the lizard.

Jump over the frog.

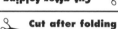 Cut after folding

✂ **Cut after folding**

and out of the zoo.

Jump, Jump, Kangaroo

 Story by Joy Cowley

Jump over the snake.

Jump, jump, kangaroo.

Jump over the dog.

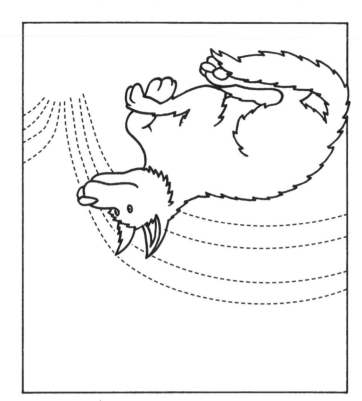

Jump, jump, kangaroo.
Jump over the fence...

and a cat.

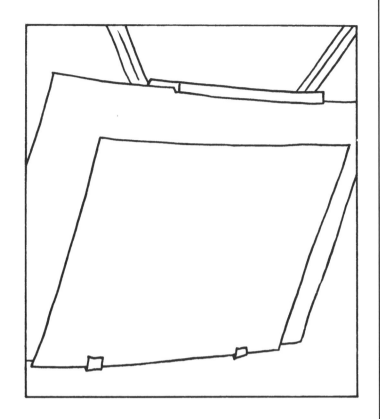

It has a sun

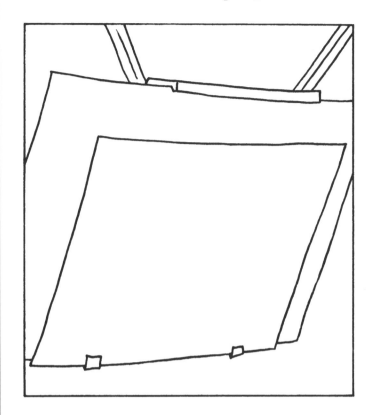

✂ Cut after folding

Note: Children may fill in the illustrations for this book.

✂ **Cut after folding**

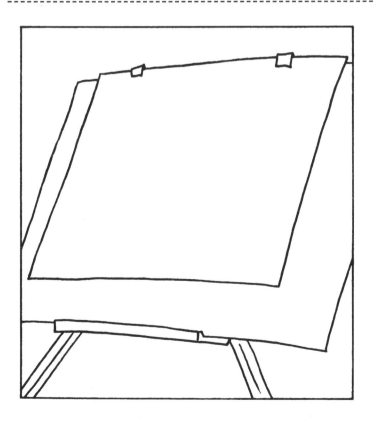

me!

My Picture

 Story by Joy Cowley

and a path.

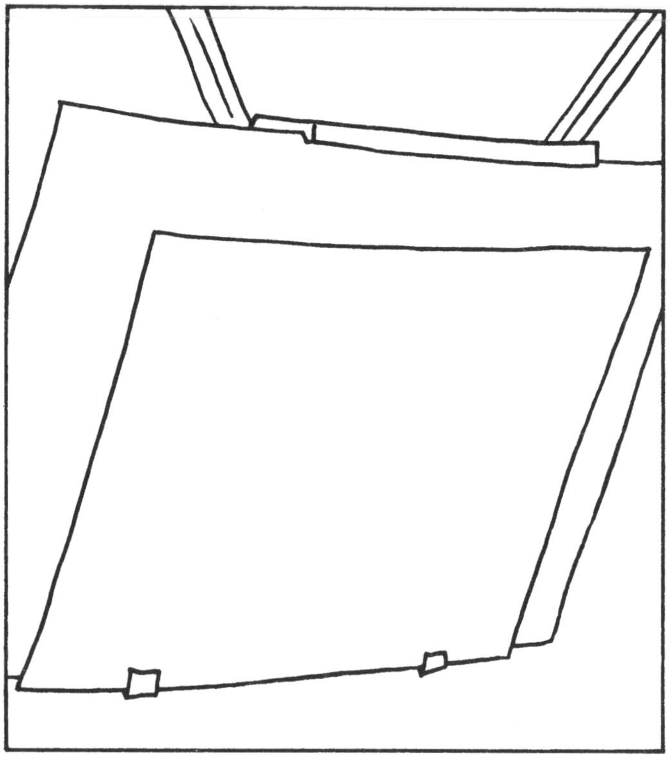

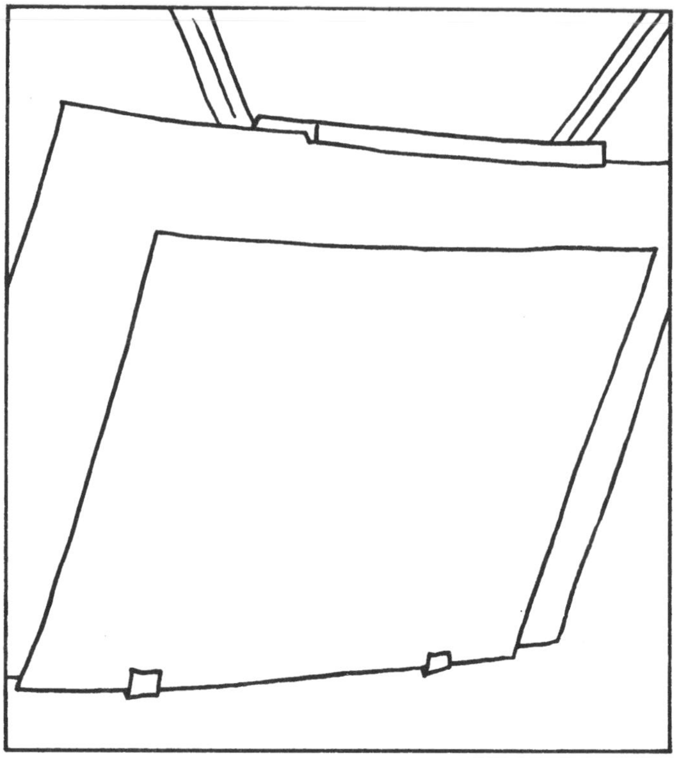

It has a tree

It has a house

and a big, **big**...

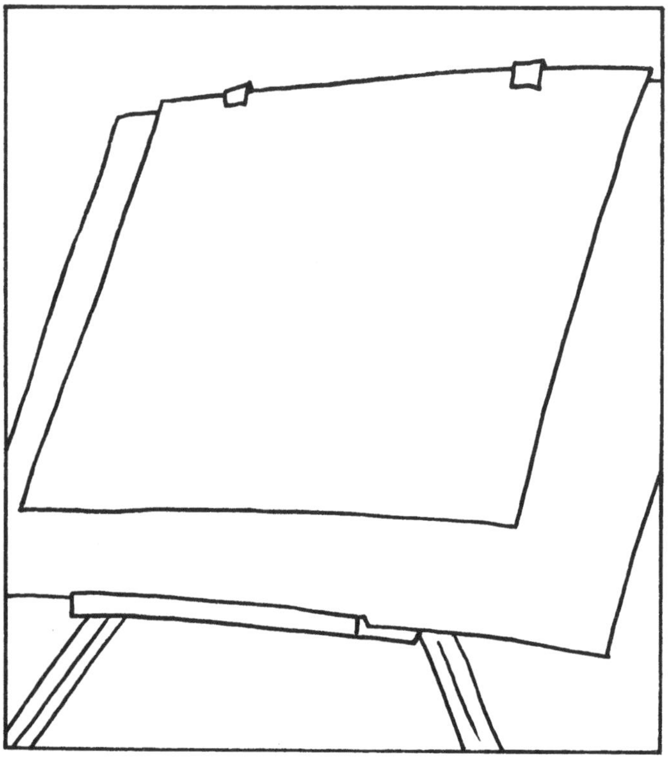

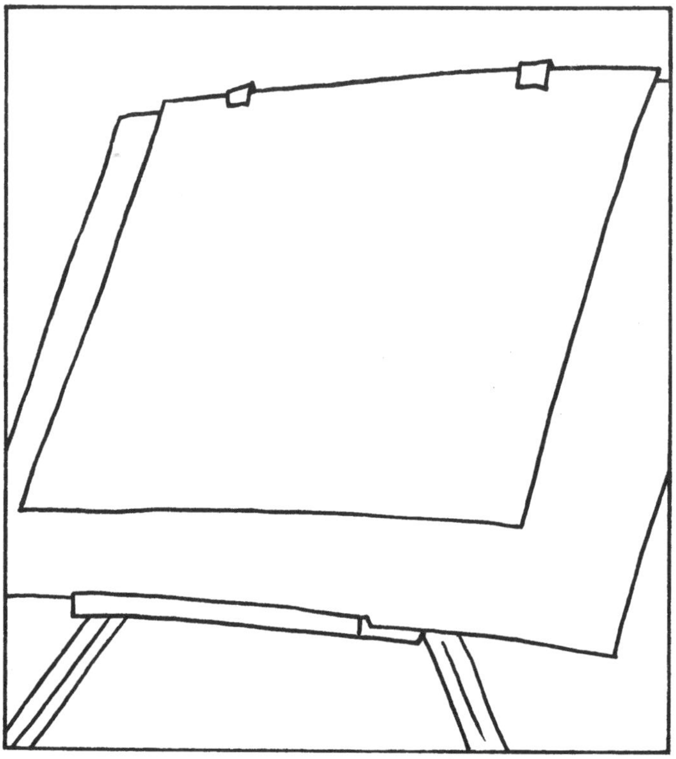

They get some hair.   They get some paper.

✂ Cut after folding

✂ **Cut after folding**

**They make a nest
for the babies there.**

The Nest

 Story by Joy Cowley

run here and there.

They get some yarn

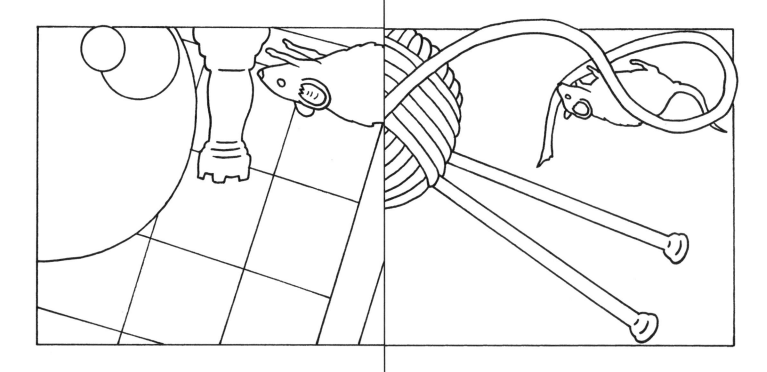

Cut after folding

Cut after folding

Mr. and Mrs. Mouse

and some teddy bear.

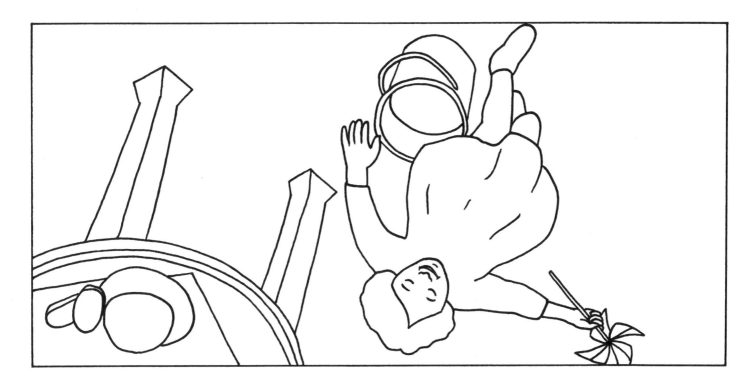

✂ Cut after folding

✂ **Cut after folding**

'Round and 'Round

**Stop, stop, Grandpa!
I feel sick.**

 Story by Joy Cowley

8

and 'round and 'round
the broom.

'Round and 'round
my Grandpa

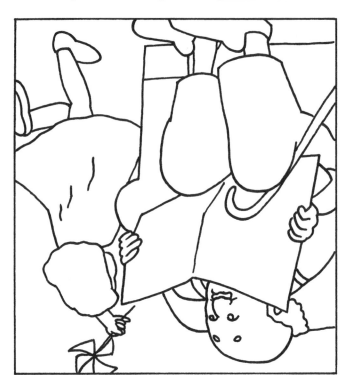

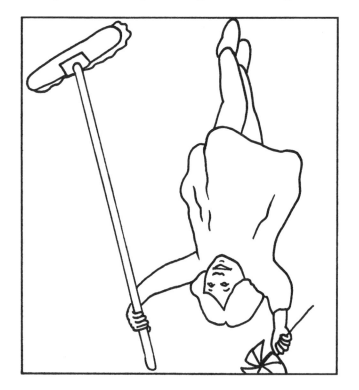

✂ Cut after folding

✂ **Cut after folding**

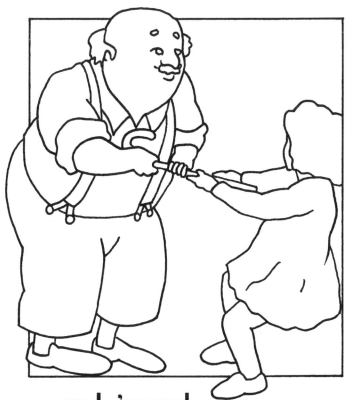

'Round and 'round
the table

and 'round
his walking stick.

I go up the tree.
You go up the tree.
You big copycat!

cats!

I go into the house.
You go into the house.

You little copycat!

Cut after folding

Cut after folding

Copycat

Story by Joy Cowley

I go down the steps.
You go down the steps.

I go down the path.
You go down the path.

Cut after folding
Cut after folding

I go up the steps.
You go up the steps.

I go up the path.
You go up the path.

▲ Copy with this side up

Mom got a bat.

Dad got a frying pan.

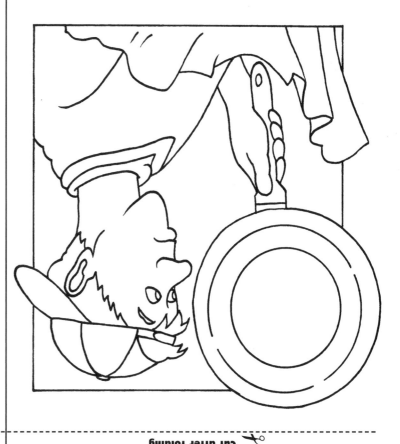

▲ Copy with this side up

Cut after folding

✂ Cut after folding

The Gifts

Mom liked the bat.

 Story by Joy Cowley

Grandpa got a hat.

Grandpa liked the hat.
Grandma liked the hammer.

▲ Copy with this side up

✂ Cut after folding

✂ Cut after folding

Grandma got a hammer.

Dad liked the frying pan.

is to take your dog
for a run.

or all of them.

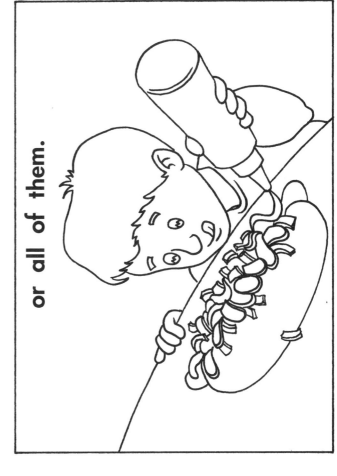

Story by Joy Cowley

How to Make
a Hot Dog

Cut after folding

Cut after folding

Put on some
pickles

or some
mustard

or some
ketchup

or some
onions

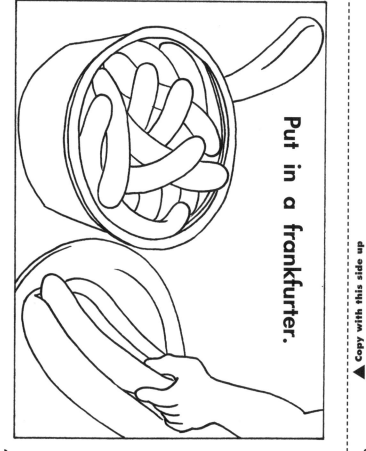

Now eat it!

✂ Cut after folding

✂ Cut after folding

The other way
to make a hot dog...

Put in a frankfurter.

To make a hot dog,
open the bun.

It can go surfing.

It can paddle a canoe.

Ice-Cream Stick

and hide.

 Story by Joy Cowley

It can play tennis.

It can make a skateboard.

What can a mouse do with an ice-cream stick?

It can dig a hole...

Four, four,
are the doors.

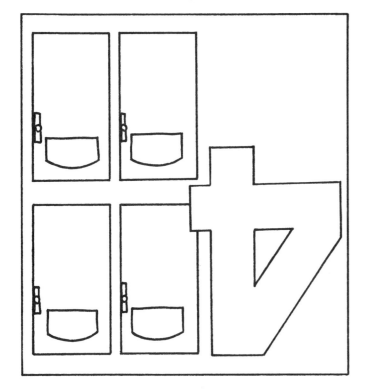

Three, three,
are the trees.

▲ **Copy with this side up**

✂ **Cut after folding**

✂ **Cut after folding**

One sun,

two shoes,

three trees,

four doors,

five hives,

six chicks.

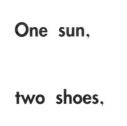

8

One, One,
Is the Sun

Story by June Melser

87

Two, two,
are the shoes.

Five, five,
are the hives.

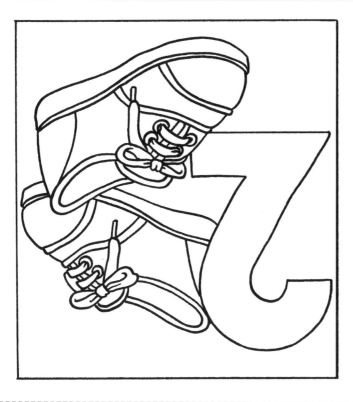

▲ Copy with this side up

✂ Cut after folding

✂ **Cut after folding**

One, one,
is the sun.

Six, six,
are the chicks.

Tick-tock.
Four o'clock.
Time for a game.

Tick-tock.
Three o'clock.
Time for a walk.

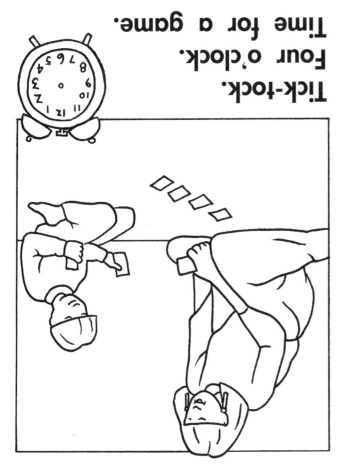

▲ Copy with this side up

Cut after folding ✂

Note: Children may draw in the hands of the clock on each page. ✂ **Cut after folding**

Tick-tock.
Seven o'clock.
Time for bed.

Tick-Tock

Story by Joy Cowley

Tick-tock.
Two o'clock.
Time for a story.

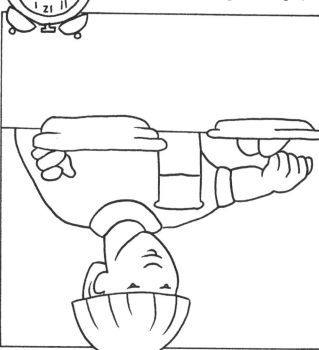

Tick-tock.
Five o'clock.
Time for dinner.

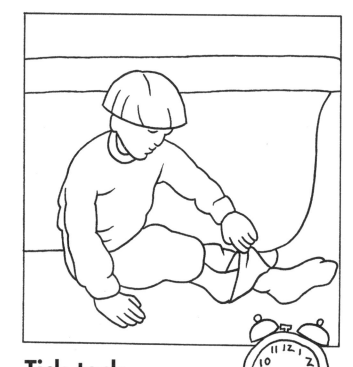

▲ Copy with this side up

✂ Cut after folding

✂ Cut after folding

Tick-tock.
One o'clock.
Time for lunch.

Tick-tock.
Six o'clock.
Time for a bath.